Sherrie Eldridge

Forever Fingerprints

An Amazing Discovery for Adopted Children

Illustrated By Rob Williams

Published by:
EMK Press,
a division of EMK Group, LLC
16 Mt Bethel Road, #219
Warren, NJ 07059
www.emkpress.com
*Known as the "Toolbox Press" we publish books for
families formed by adoption. We also raise funds
for children who remain in orphanages worldwide,
and for post adoption support for families.*

text ©2007 Sherrie Eldridge
illustrations ©2007 Rob Williams

Publisher's Cataloging-in-Publication Data

Eldridge, Sherrie.
Forever fingerprints : an amazing discovery for adopted
children / by Sherrie Eldridge ; illustrated by Rob Williams
      p. cm.
      ISBN 9780972624435
      Summary: Lucie's aunt and uncle are having a baby,
which makes Lucie wonder about her birth mother and
what it was like before she was born.
[1. Adoption--Fiction. 2. Mother and child--Fiction. 3.
Adopted children --Fiction. 4. Birth mothers--Fiction.
5. Birth parents--Fiction.] I. Williams, Rob, 1951-. II. Title.

PZ7.E3845 Fo 2007
[E]--dc22   2007924553

Printed in China

printed on acid free paper, reinforced binding

EMK Press titles currently in print:

*Adoption Parenting: Creating a Toolbox,
Building Connections*
Edited by Jean MacLeod and Sheena Macrae

I Don't Have Your Eyes
by Carrie Kitze

What My Parents Couldn't Tell Me
a book by adoptees for adopted teens
edited by EMK Press

We See the Moon
by Carrie Kitze

*At Home in This World,
A China Adoption Story*
by Jean MacLeod

We provide tools for adoptive families including
books and a wealth of resources and
web links on our site that are available for free
download. Visit our website to sign up for our free
monthly newsletter on topics of interest to
adoptive families and the professionals
who work with them.

www.emkpress.com

To reach us via email: info@emkpress.com

Other Titles by Sherrie Eldridge:
*Twenty Things Adopted Kids Wish Their Adoptive
Parents Knew*

*Twenty Life-Transforming Choices Adoptees
Need to Make*

Dear Parents,

As an adult adoptee, how I wish my parents and I could have enjoyed a book like **Forever Fingerprints!**

Forever Fingerprints provides a creative way for you to help your child integrate his sense of connection to the past and present! Lucie's story will resonate within the heart of your child and provide a springboard for him to ask questions. When Lucie's pregnant aunt comes for a visit, many curiosities surface and her parents demonstrate radiant love by addressing issues openly. They then tell Lucie that she can feel close to her birth parents even though they aren't present. How? By teaching her the precious meaning of fingerprints! They are a physical tie to her birth parents because they were created in her birth mother's womb and will never change.

Lucie's parents also demonstrate the art of honoring their child's birth parents. They rejoice with her when she finds the sense of connection to her birth parents and kiss her fingertips along with her. They know that when they honor her birth parents, they are honoring Lucie.

Your child will likely travel twisting roads before reaching an understanding of his life experience. This story book will help you consider future questions and how to clarify information so that your child has an accurate understanding of the information surrounding his adoption.

I know that you are like Lucie's parents! More than anything, you want to help your child understand their beginnings. May this book be a tool in your hands to help accomplish that wonderful end!

With warm regards,

Sherrie Eldridge

When Lucie woke up, she remembered that Uncle John and Aunt Grace were coming with a great big surprise. She wiggled her toes, jumped out of bed, and danced into her clothes. Her mom fixed sunshine yellow scrambled eggs, juice, and toast with purple jelly.

But Lucie wasn't hungry because there were butterflies in her tummy.

They will calm down, her mom told her, *if you feed them your breakfast.*

The butterflies ate the scrambled eggs and they drank the juice. They ate everything except the toast with the yummy purple jelly. But the jelly was Lucie's favorite part so she scooped it off with her fingers and licked each one–round and round and up and down.

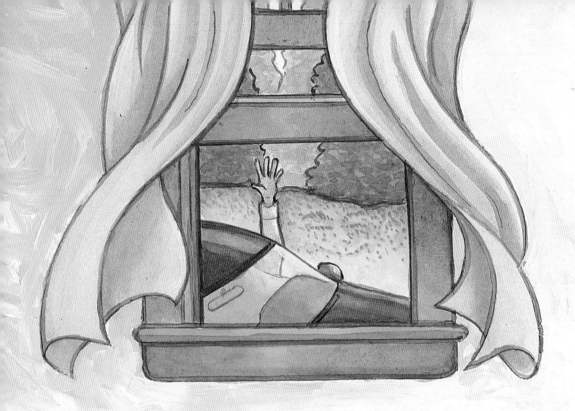

Lucie wanted to look fairy princess special for her
aunt and uncle.

Her lavender dress, high heels, and sparkly crown would be
perfect! Swirling and twirling to music, she dreamed about
the **BIG** surprise.

BEEP...beep-beep-beep!

Lucie raced lickety-split to meet them, with arms stretched
high to Aunt Grace for hugs.

BOING...BOING!

What was that? She tried again....

BOING-I-TY...BOING...BOING!

WHOA!!!

It was Aunt Grace's tummy.
It was so **FAT!**
What had she been eating? *Watermelons?*
Uncle John swooped Lucie up in his arms
and whispered the surprise in her ear.
A **REAL** baby was growing inside Aunt
Grace's tummy.

YAHOO!!!
Lucie jumped down, kicked off her high heels,
and turned cartwheels around the yard.

Later Aunt Grace asked if Lucie wanted to feel the baby.

Lucie's eyes about popped out of her head when Aunt Grace pulled up her red blouse.

WOW! Her tummy looked like a beach ball!

Hand-in-hand, they pushed on her tummy.
Lucie felt little taps on her fingertips.

OH, MY GOODNESS!

It was the baby tapping on
Aunt Grace's tummy
from the inside!

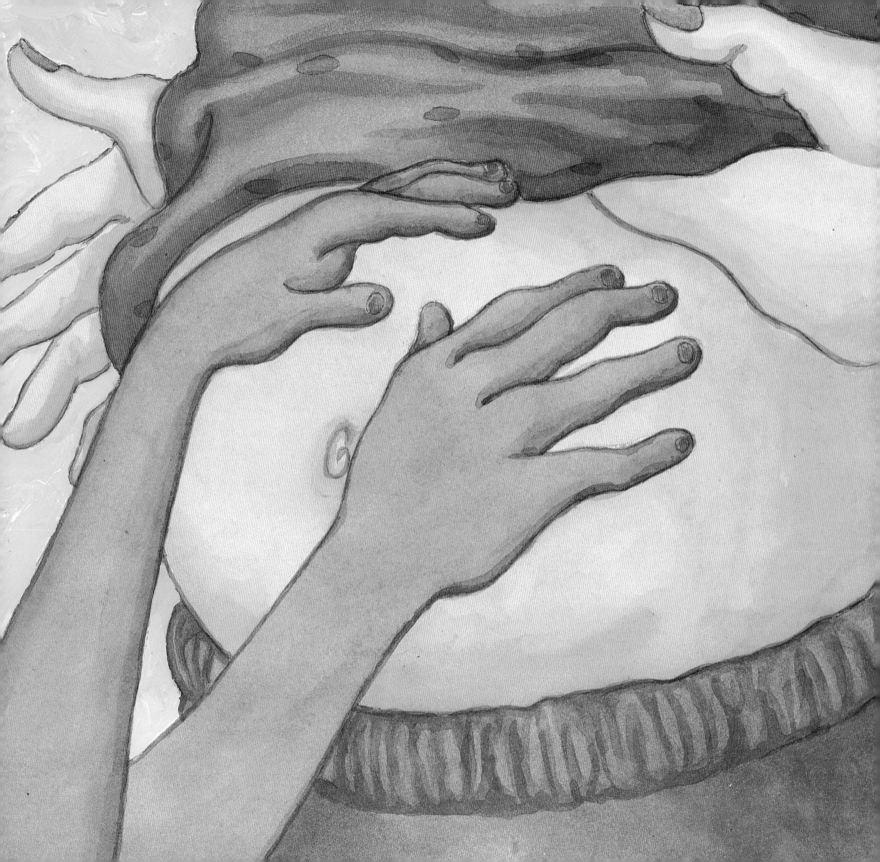

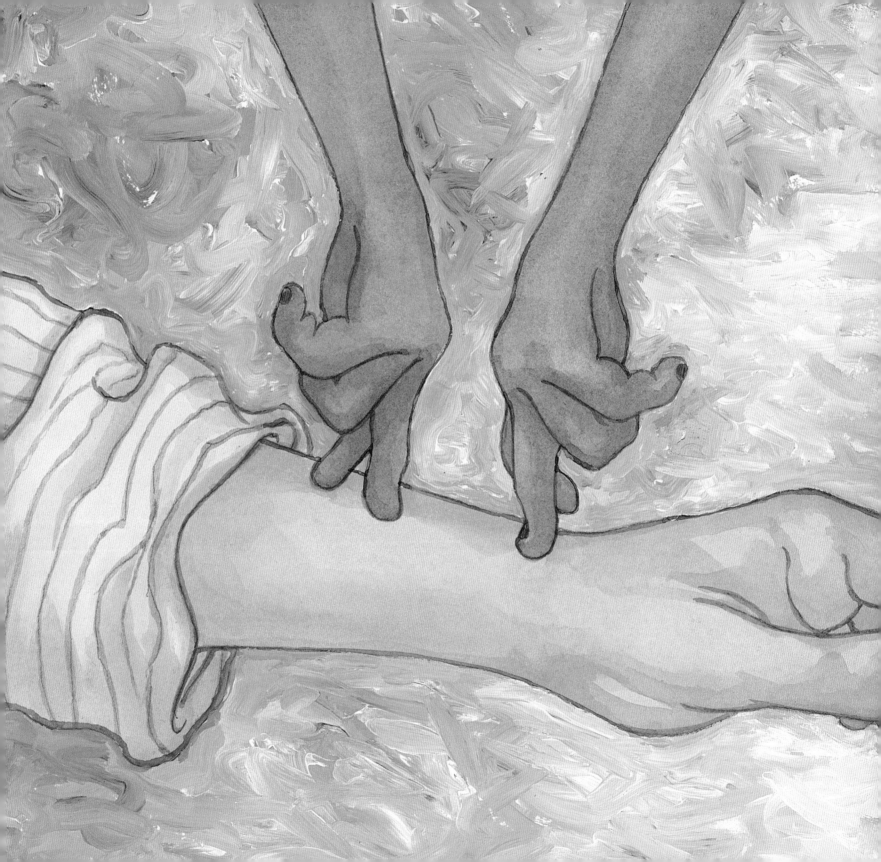

All day long Lucie wondered what the baby was doing.
Was he eating?
Was he sleeping?
Was he pooping?

If he was pooping, **where did the poop go?**

Did it turn into pizza???

That night, she moved her
fingertips on her dad's arm, like
an itsy-bitsy spider going up a
water spout. She wanted
to show him how it felt
when the baby kicked.

The next day Lucie and her friend, Cole, made fingerprint pictures. Lucie added a head, arms, legs, and feet.

TAAA-DAAA!
It was Auntie Grace's baby!

As they pushed their fingers into the stamp pad and then onto the paper, they noticed that each of their fingers made a different print. Some had loops and some seemed to swirl round and round.

Then Cole noticed that the prints made by Lucie were different from his.

That night, before bedtime, Lucie dove into bed and yanked the covers over her head.

Lucie had new questions about her adoption after being with Aunt Grace and the baby. She knew that everyone has a birth mother and birth father. She knew she grew in her birth mother's tummy and that some kids live with their birth parents after they're born, and some don't. Lucie had dreamed that hers were a king and a queen who lived in a beautiful castle.

But if her birth parents lived in a castle, why didn't they keep her?

Was she too big, too small…did she cry too much, or what? How could they not love her enough to keep her? She must have been really **BAD**. Lucie hit her pillow—

Boom! Boom! Boom!

Lucie was sad and screamed that she wanted to grow in her mom's tummy. She wanted to know whose fingers had felt her tapping before she was born.

Lucie's mom picked her up and cuddled her in the rocking chair softly telling her it wasn't her fault— it was a decision made by her birth parents for big people reasons. Unbuttoning her shirt, she tucked it around Lucie while they rocked, back and forth, back and forth. Her mom sang:

You were and are a good baby,
With perfect fingers and toes,
A head full of soft fuzzy hair,
And an adorable, kissable nose.

Then she wrapped Lucie's hands in hers and blew warm kisses on them.

Lucie asked her dad to tell her again how she got in her birth mother's tummy. He said that there is a special way a man and woman come together to make babies. Every baby grows in a little pouch called a womb—a place in a mother's body made just for a baby. It stretches as the baby grows, so the little one will always have enough room and always be safe. There is even a warm sack of water around the baby to keep it snug until it is time to be born.

Lucie giggled.
She wondered if the water had fish in it.

Lucie loved thinking about being in her birth mother's womb.
It was her first home.

The sound of her birth mother's heartbeat made baby Lucie feel comfy-cozy. All the super-duper things about her birth mother and father were mixed together to make Lucie.

Maybe her love for horses came from her birth father and her pretty-as-a-picture smile from her birth mother?

Lucie asked if she could meet her birth parents. She wanted to know what they were like. Her mom and dad didn't know what they were like or how to find them.

Tears filled Lucie's eyes.
Her mom and dad felt sad too.

Then her dad grabbed her fingers and told her that they had something special for her—something that they had been waiting for just the right time to tell her...
something about her fingertips.

Lucie's eyes got **BIG!**

Her fingertips had been so busy.

They felt the new baby kick,
and tickled her dad,
and made a fingerprint drawing.

WAIT!

There was **SOMETHING MORE** Lucie had to learn!

No one in the **whole world** has fingerprints exactly like hers. Other parts of her body will change, but not her fingertips. They would forever be the same. Lucie turned her hands upside down and she saw the loops and squiggles of her fingerprints again.

Now her fingertips looked like ten **GOOOOORGEEEOUS** flowers.
Lucie grinned from ear-to-ear.

STOP! *Lucie needs to hear the rest of the story!*

The best part about Lucie's fingertips is that they were created while she was snug inside her birth mother's womb. She was **SO** close to her then and can be close to her **NOW** and **FOREVER**.

HOW? Lucie squealed.

All Lucie needed to do was look at her fingertips
and remember her birth mother, just like when she was in
her birth mother's womb.

Her fingers would never look the same to her again.

Lucie squeezed her fingertips close together,
pushed them to her lips, and planted teeny, tiny
kisses on each one. With every kiss, she felt roastier
and toastier inside.

Then her parents planted kisses all over her fingertips.

Later, when she went to sleep, Lucie tucked her fingertips close to her heart.

She dreamed that she was in a circle with her mom and dad and her birth mother and father. It was a wonderful circle that included *all her family*.

While she knew it was a dream, Lucie realized that no matter what, they were all related to her in different ways and they were all a part of her very own, very special extended family.

Using Forever Fingerprints: Parent Tools and Activities

As you read **Forever Fingerprints,** you will see there is more to the sweet story of connection that Sherrie Eldridge created than meets the eye. It's about how babies grow in their mom's tummy, and how adopted children have a forever connection to their birth parents through their fingertips. It's a wonderful tool to open the door for more loving conversations and truthful discussions about how you and your child came to be a family.

As any child grows, they wonder about their beginnings. As our adopted children grow, the answers to basic questions of "did I grow in your tummy, mommy?" lead us to start discussions about their adoption stories, and how the baby got in there. For all children this is a normal part of figuring out their place in the family and often a pregnant relative or friend will be the springboard for these discussions, like with Lucie and her Aunt Grace. For many of us parents, this is the discussion we have been dreading. If we introduce them to birth parents, will they love and want them more?

The reality is that kids know who all the parts of their families are. They can make sense of different relationships, they know who fits in what slot. They know who takes care of them and loves them every day. And they depend on us, as their parents, to help them to make sense of something that can be pretty hard to understand when you are 5 or 6 or 7–the concept of adoption and the bittersweetness that surrounds it. To get the family they have, one had to give them up. That can be tough stuff for our children and we need to know how to catch them like Lucie's parents, in a supportive and loving way that is open to any discussion our child needs to have with

us. We do want to claim our children as our own, but in claiming all the parts of them, including their extended families–their birth families, our circle of love and understanding is expanded, not diminished.

We suggest that you read this book first to help you be prepared for questions that might arise during the reading or after.

So what questions might arise as children read this book with you?

Some of the questions that you may find will be 'what-ifs', questions about what it would be like for your child to have stayed with birth family. They also may be about your child's yearning to meet birth parents and learn more what they are like. Some questions may be about your child's grief and anger at loss, loss of their first family and the chance to be parented by the ones who gave birth to them. Other questions might include where their place in the family lies, who are their relatives and how does it all fit. For some children, this book will bring to life the very real understanding in a concrete way that they were born. Many have heard their adoption story, but not their birth story.

And what questions might arise for you as you read this book?

As parents, we need to come to terms with the parts of the story of how our children came to be with us that are hard to hear or that trigger our own feelings. Pregnancy questions can be hard for some of those who have experienced infertility. Suggesting a connection between yourself and your child's birth parents might be hard. You might be concerned by the idea of connection, either real or emotional. Maybe there are hard truths in the past of your child and the reality of the story is difficult to deal with. Or your child has birth siblings who are currently being parented by his birth parents. There could be many difficult truths that stop us as parents from talking about our children's past and their birth history. It is our job as parents to make sense of our own issues so that we can move beyond them and help our children. Tools like this book can help both parent and child.

Reading the Book

Some children will stop you as you read to ask questions while others will ponder and have their questions come out later. Still others might feel out of sorts and cover that up with silliness like Lucie does. Every child is different. Older children may listen keenly as the book is read to a younger sibling, taking their own understanding of the information presented in this book. Other children will read this story over and over looking for things hidden in the pictures and in the words. For each child, being able to hold them close and answer any questions they have with honesty and love is the most important gift we can give our children. Each time you read this story, your child will come away with a little more.

Activities for Later

You may want to use fingerprint stamping as a tool for further discussion. The fingerprint tool is powerful and art is a marvellous way to describe feelings and thoughts too complicated for words in young children.

You may want to talk with your children about feelings and loss–use daily life for this, pets, disagreements with school friends or siblings. Another useful tool to talk to your child about connections is to use lifebooks, pictures, and photos that relate to their pre-adoption history.

Forever Fingerprints offers more, much more, for you and your adopted child. It can be read on many levels, from simple story to springboard narrative for your child and you to ponder on birth parents. It can start you on the path of developing narratives about your child's connection to first family and to you. This book allows us to explore the fears both we and our children have about being an adoptive family. It allows us to celebrate the joy that being connected brings. We parents share that gift with our children by helping them understand that they are safe with us, and safe in the understanding that we can help them navigate the big feelings that adoption can bring.

For more ideas on opening the dialog with your children, visit the Forever Fingerprints blog at the EMK Press website (www.emkpress.com). There you can ask Sherrie Eldridge questions and get answers, read comments from other parents, and see what may work for your family and circumstance. Also, the parent resources section of the EMK Press website has additional informational guides from a number of notable adoption professionals to help you as you work with your children to understand the complexities of adoption.

Carrie Kitze and Sheena Macrae, PhD.
Publisher and Senior Editor, EMK Press

A little something about fingerprints...

The outer layer of skin on our fingers has a series of ridges on it forming special patterns we call fingerprints. Everybody has a special-to-them set of fingerprints, and patterns can run in families. Fingerprint ridges form on babies' fingers while in the womb, around the third and the fourth month of development. Identical twins start out with the same general patterns on their fingertips, but with how fast they grow inside their mom, their position inside the womb, and how much they move around creates differences in the patterns.

Once fully developed, the pattern of ridges never change, even as the finger grows. Think about drawing a picture on a balloon and then blowing it up. The picture just grows larger but doesn't change. That's what happens to your fingerprints as you grow.

There are three main patterns that are found on fingertips: the arch, the loop, and the whorl. Which kinds do you have? The loop is the most common. In some families, they have the same kind of pattern on the same fingers which means that fingerprints are hereditary. Hereditary means that some physical characteristic is passed from biological parent to child. If you have a swirl on one of your fingertips, either your birth mom or birth dad might have that too. The size of your fingertips and the shape of them has a lot to do with what basic pattern will appear on your finger.

The best way to see what your fingerprints look like is to use a stamp pad. Be careful not to smudge them! Have an adult help you to roll a finger on a stamp pad. Then you repeat the process on clean white paper. Make sure to clean your fingers before you touch other things. Your parents have experience with fingerprinting because they had to have their fingerprints taken as part of the paperwork to adopt you!

You can make fun figures with fingerprints. There are some ideas scattered in this book. What can you think of to make?

whorl

loop

arch